Christmas Piano Solos.

CW00540286

Wise Publications
London/New York/Paris/Sydney/Copenhagen/Madrid

Exclusive Distributors:
Music Sales Limited
8/9 Frith Street,
London W1V 5TZ, England.
Music Sales Pty Limited
120 Rothschild Avenue,
Rosebery, NSW 2018,
Australia.

Music arranged by Frank Booth
Book design by Studio Twenty, London
Computer management by Adam Hay Editorial Design
Music processed by MSS Studios

Music Sales' complete catalogue describes thousands of titles and
is available in full colour sections by subject, direct from
Music Sales Limited. Please state your areas of interest and send a
cheque/postal order for £1.50 for postage to:
Music Sales Limited, Newmarket Road,
Bury St. Edmunds, Suffolk IP33 3YB.

Your Guarantee of Quality
As publishers, we strive to produce every book to the
highest commercial standards.
The music has been freshly engraved and the book has
been carefully designed to minimise awkward page turns and
to make playing from it a real pleasure.
Particular care has been given to specifying acid-free, neutral-sized
paper made from pulps which have not been elemental chlorine
bleached. This pulp is from farmed sustainable forests and was
produced with special regard for the environment.
Throughout, the printing and binding have been planned to
ensure a sturdy, attractive publication which should give
years of enjoyment.
If your copy fails to meet our high standards,
please inform us and we will gladly replace it.

Printed in the United Kingdom by
Caligraving Limited, Thetford, Norfolk.

A ROOT'N TOOT'N SANTA CLAUS

Words & Music by Oakley Haldeman & Peter Tinturin.

Fairly bright tempo

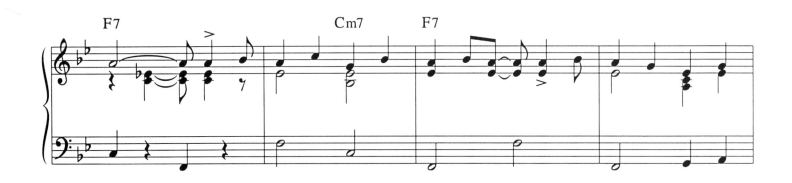

AWAY IN A MANGER

Traditional Christmas Carol.

CAROL OF THE DRUM

Words & Music by Katherine K. Davies.

DECK THE HALLS

Traditional.

CHRISTMAS ALPHABET

Words & Music by Buddy Kaye & Jules Loman.

DING DONG MERRILY ON HIGH

Traditional.

Fairly bright tempo

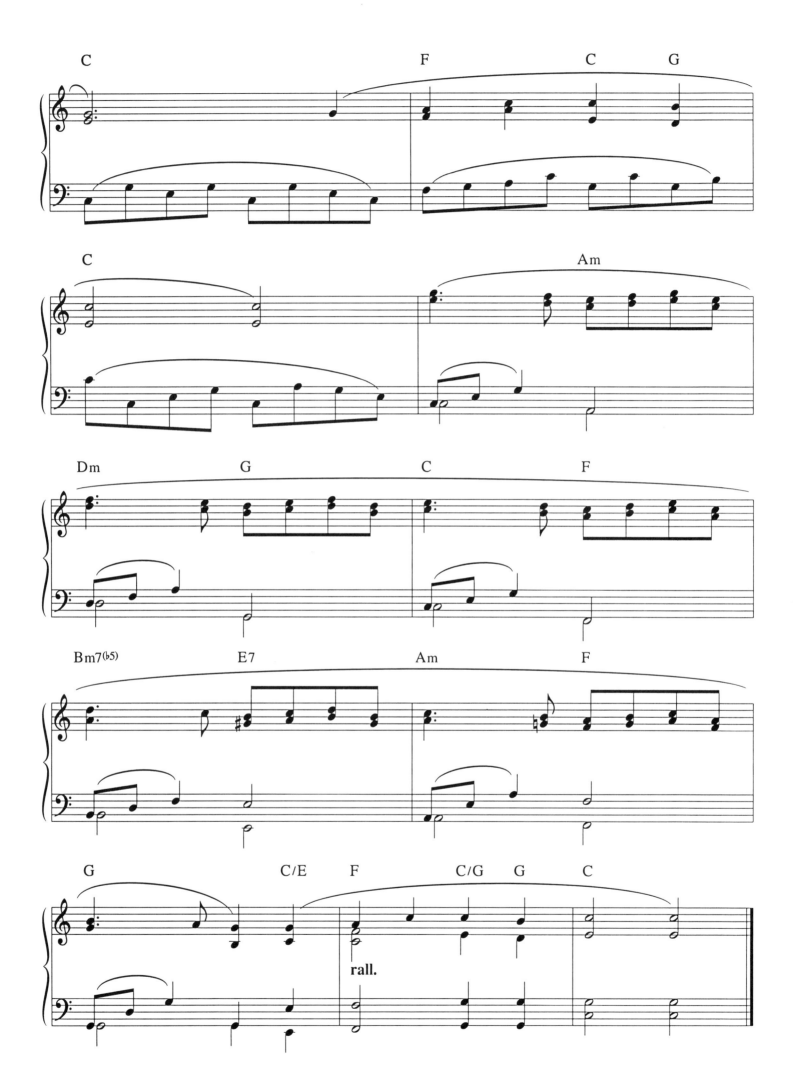

FROSTY THE SNOWMAN

Words & Music by Steve Nelson & Jack Rollins.

HAPPY XMAS (WAR IS OVER)

Words & Music by John Lennon & Yoko Ono.

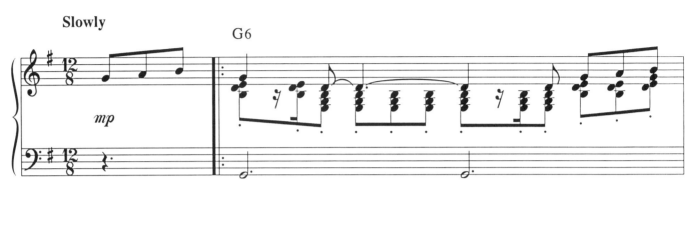

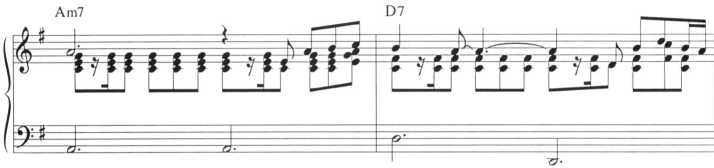

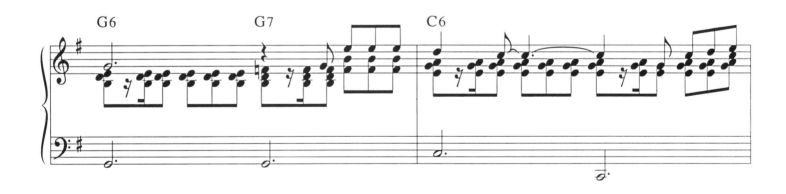

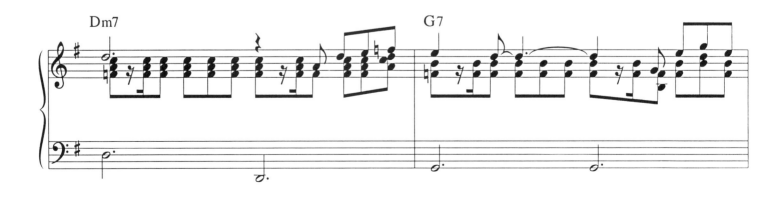

HERE COMES SANTA CLAUS

Words & Music by Gene Autry & Oakley Haldeman.

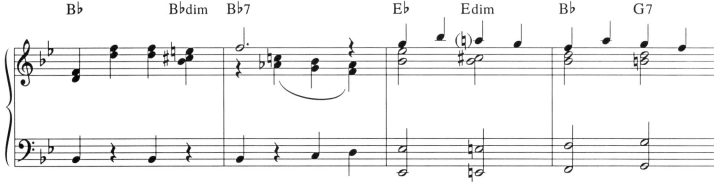

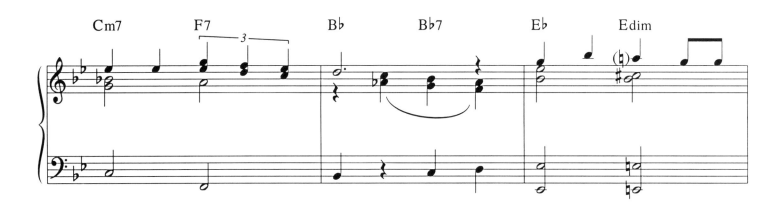

23

I WISH IT COULD BE CHRISTMAS EVERY DAY

Words & Music by Roy Wood.

Moderately with a beat

GOOD KING WENCESLAS

Traditional Christmas Carol.

IT CAME UPON A MIDNIGHT CLEAR

Music by Richard Storrs Willis. Words by Edmund Hamilton Sears.

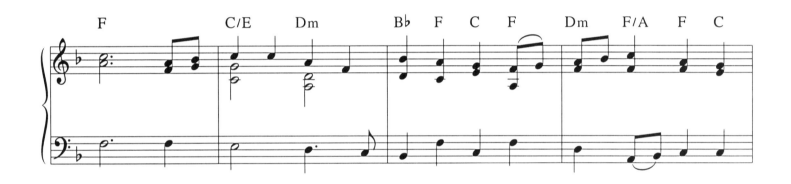

IT'S GONNA BE A COLD COLD CHRISTMAS

Words & Music by Roger Greenaway & Geoff Stephens.

LET THERE BE PEACE ON EARTH

Words & Music by Sy Miller & Jill Jackson.

35

JINGLE BELLS

Traditional.

Steady 2 beat

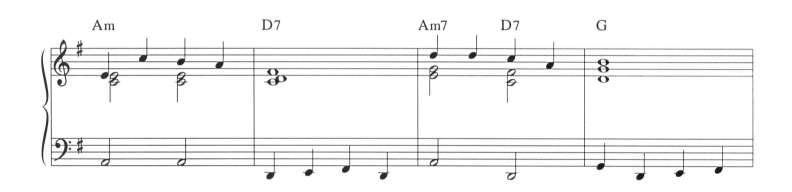

MARY'S BOY CHILD

Words & Music by Jester Hairston.

O CHRISTMAS TREE (O TANNENBAUM)

Christmas Carol.

MERRY XMAS EVERYBODY

Words & Music by Neville Holder & James Lea.

MISTLETOE AND WINE

Music by Keith Strachan. Words by Leslie Stewart & Jeremy Paul.

O COME ALL YE FAITHFUL

Traditional.

O LITTLE TOWN OF BETHLEHEM

Traditional Christmas Carol.

ONCE IN ROYAL DAVID'S CITY

Traditional Christmas Carol.

SILENT NIGHT

Words & Music by Joseph Mohr & Franz Gruber.

SNOWY WHITE SNOW AND JINGLE BELLS

Words & Music by Billy Reid, Johnny Sheridan, Ralph Ruvin, Harold Irving & Dennis Berger.
© Copyright 1949 Billy Reid Publishing Limited.
Rights assigned to Campbell Connelly & Company Limited, 8/9 Frith Street, London W1.
All Rights Reserved. International Copyright Secured.

STEP INTO CHRISTMAS

Words & Music by Elton John & Bernie Taupin.

Moderately

THE FIRST NOWELL

Traditional.

THE HOLLY AND THE IVY

Traditional.

THE TWELVE DAYS OF CHRISTMAS

Traditional Christmas Song.

repeat this bar as
often as required

1.-6.

Last

rit.

60

WE THREE KINGS OF ORIENT ARE

Traditional.

WHILE SHEPHERDS WATCHED THEIR FLOCKS BY NIGHT

Traditional.

Each volume is specially arranged by Stephen Duro in extra-easy keys, so that the music fits comfortably to your hands, and includes lyrics (where appropriate) and chord symbols.

Collect the full series...

Abba *Order No. AM91038*
Bach *Order No. AM91041*
Ballads *Order No. AM89944*
Beethoven *Order No. AM91042*
Blues *Order No. AM91507*
Children's Songs *Order No. AM89953*
Richard Clayderman *Order No. AM91501*
Classics *Order No. AM89927*

Simply, the easiest
books of popular music
for piano ever!

Christmas *Order No. AM91509*
Folk Songs *Order No. AM91366*
Handel *Order No. AM91299*
Love Themes *Order No. AM91508*
Marches *Order No. AM91365*
Mozart *Order No. AM91043*
Operatic Arias *Order No. AM91312*
Pops *Order No. AM89939*
Rock 'n' Roll *Order No. AM91040*
Show Tunes *Order No. AM91039*
Symphonic Themes *Order No. AM91313*
Hits of the 50s *Order No. AM91502*
Hits of the 60s *Order No. AM91503*
Hits of the 70s *Order No. AM91504*
Hits of the 80s *Order No. AM91505*
The Beatles *Order No. AM89912*
The Beatles 2 *Order No. NO90571*
The Carpenters *Order No. AM91500*
TV Themes *Order No. AM89968*
Viennese Waltzes *Order No. AM91314*

Available from all good music shops

In case of difficulty, please contact:
Music Sales Limited
Newmarket Road,
Bury St. Edmunds,
Suffolk IP33 3YB, England
Telephone: 0284 702600
Fax: 0284 768301

The Beatles

Enya

Phil Collins

Van Morrison

Bob Dylan

Sting

Paul Simon

Tracy Chapman

Eric Clapton

Pink Floyd

New Kids On The Block

Bryan Adams

Tina Turner

Elton John

Bee Gees

Whitney Houston

AC/DC

Bringing you the
words

All the latest in rock and pop. Plus the brightest and best in West End show scores. Music books for every instrument under the sun. And exciting new teach-yourself ideas like "Let's Play Keyboard" - in cassette/book packs, or on video. Available from all good music shops.

and
music

Music Sales' complete catalogue lists thousands of titles and is available free from your local music shop, or direct from Music Sales Limited. Please send a cheque or postal order for £1.50 (for postage) to:

Music Sales Limited
Newmarket Road,
Bury St Edmunds,
Suffolk IP33 3YB

Buddy

Five Guys Named Moe

Les Misérables

West Side Story

Phantom Of The Opera

Show Boat

The Rocky Horror Show

**Bringing you the
world's best music.**